WHAT'S ECOLOGY?

by

Clifford C. Humphrey

Director, Ecology Action Educational Institute

and

Robert G. Evans

72-4795

Contents

ECOLOGY ACTION EDUCATIONAL INSTITUTE

Clifford Humphrey founded the Ecology Action Educational Institute in February 1968 in Modesto, California. It was incorporated as a non-profit organization to "study and develop methods for the creation of a balanced relationship between the needs and aspirations of society and the limitations of man's environment." The staff of the institute, under Mr. Humphrey's direction, have prepared a large traveling exhibit, participated in the creation of this book, written many articles on ecology, inspired the founding of 200 similar groups across the country, and spoken before many influential groups including a United Nations committee and the American Association for the Advancement of Science.

Ecology Action is dedicated to clearly explaining the ecological imperatives to the general public and motivating individuals to take action to preserve the environment. For more information and specific recommendations for actions you can take, you may write:

Ecology Action Educational Institute
Box 3895
Modesto, California 95352

Robert Evans is a high school teacher and a curriculum consultant on ecology and environmental subjects for the Sonoma County (California) Public School System.

In the interest of conserving our natural resources and in the spirit of the ecological principles set forth in the following pages, the paper selected for use in this book is a recycled paper. It has been manufactured from reclaimed waste papers that would otherwise have been burned, used for landfill or simply thrown away as litter. The paper was provided by the Bergstrom Paper Company, Neenah, Wisconsin, a mill that has been recycling paper for more than 60 years.

recycled  paper

CHAPTER ONE

Principles
of Ecology

On December 5, 1969, a California newspaper, the *Contra Costa Times,* in an article headlined "Moraga Kids Wage Smog War," reported that instead of riding cars to school as usual, 1,600 Moraga High School students "rode horses, pedaled bicycles and walked for miles along hilly roads to demonstrate against air pollution. They carried hand-lettered signs such as 'STOP POLLUTION,' 'STOP YOUR ENGINE,' 'SMOG IS A GAS,' and 'SUPPORT SMOG-FREE DAY.' "

A few weeks earlier, a number of nursing mothers had discovered that their infants were ingesting milk with a higher DDT content than is tolerated in cows' milk by the U.S. Department of Public Health. These mothers were understandably concerned and, at a press conference, expressed their feelings of helplessness.

The Pollack brothers have published a book entitled *Famine 1975,* expanding on the thesis that with the world's population exploding at its present rate, and with the food supply remaining relatively constant, global famines will inevitably strike before 1980.

Scientists and technologists warn daily that we are running out of aluminum, petroleum, water, and other limited natural resources. The newspapers headline such "eco-disasters" as massive oil spills, mercury poisoning, danger from radioactivity, the draining of the Everglades, imminent famines, and the extinction of several species of birds and animals.

Many thoughtful people have become alarmed over the threat that contamination, depletion, and overcrowding pose to their survival. This book is designed to define the nature of our problem, and suggest alternatives to the present critical situation.

Ecology is the science concerned with the relationship between organisms and their environment and the interrelationships and

1

Makeup of Earth's surface

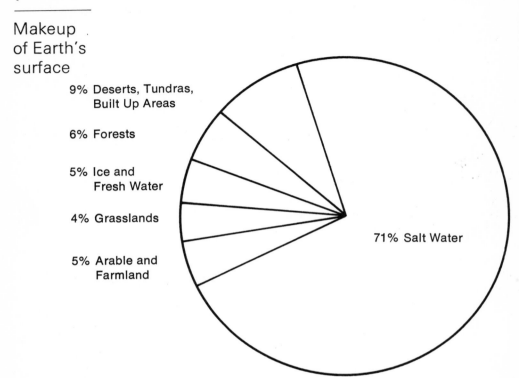

9% Deserts, Tundras, Built Up Areas

6% Forests

5% Ice and Fresh Water

4% Grasslands

5% Arable and Farmland

71% Salt Water

This graph shows the percentage of the earth covered by each type of surface. This makeup forms the basic limitation to human population.

interdependencies of these organisms. The word *ecology* means (in Greek) "knowledge of the household," a household shared by all forms of life. Such knowledge includes all the relationships, processes, and energy sources of all living communities. The entire planet is the proper subject in the science of ecology, including its radioactive decay over billions of years, its liquid-like center, its gravity, its diverse cultures, the tides, and all organic and inorganic materials.

As a means of better understanding the intricate relationship between organisms and their environment, let us examine an ecosystem in which fish are the most central element. An *ecosystem* is an easily definable group of organisms and their immediate environment, such as, a meadow, a pond, or a grassy field. The organisms' survival depends on a delicate balance of energy, food, and all the other factors important to the system's existence. An ecologist studying trout in a mountain stream would be concerned with water flow, water temperature, and insect life in the pools and rapids, as these are the major elements of the trout's "household."

The ecologist must also be aware of the many seemingly unrelated factors that could affect the trout's ecosystem, such as an unusually dry winter or a new logging road across a stream. The dry winter would result in a sparse snow pack that could in turn lead to a shortage of cold water to cool the streams adequately during the warm summer months. Since oxygen is less soluble in warm water, the fish would be threatened with "suffocation." A logging road that fords the creek could result in heavy siltation. This contamination of the stream with dirt could destroy the insects that the trout feed on. The trout population subjected to both a dry winter and a busy logging road would certainly diminish in number and possibly perish if those conditions persisted.

2

Basic volumes

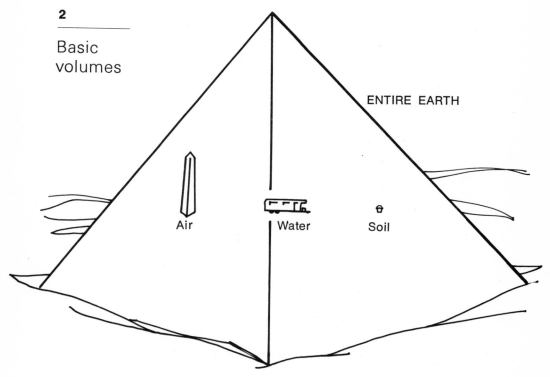

This illustration compares the volume of the entire planet (100,000,000 cubic units) with the three basic components of the biosphere; air (35,000 cubic units), water (6,000 cubic units) and soil (1 cubic unit).

Most ecosystems are durable. They can maintain their structure as long as all the contributing factors remain present within them. As conditions change, different organisms may dominate the ecosystem; a dry summer may mean that one plant in a meadow exists in greater numbers than another, but both species continue to exist within that ecosystem. A wetter year could reverse the relative plant or insect populations in terms of greater and lesser numbers, but the meadow will contain all of the same ingredients as long as the natural sequence of events continues. Such things as wet years, dry years, tropical storms, floods, or fires put enormous pressure on ecosystems, but they recover.

Although ecosystems can survive harsh and drastic natural events, they are still exceedingly fragile. The addition or elimination of only one factor in the environment can cause the collapse of that ecosystem and the subsequent organization of a completely new ecosystem. Such natural occurrences as volcanic eruptions, landslides, or an earthquake could wipe out an ecosystem. In this modern, technologically advanced time, however, changes caused by man are more frequent, more damaging, and more widespread than those caused by natural phenomena. The ecological changes brought about by man are more pertinent to the current study of ecology.

THE BIOSPHERE AND ITS SELF-REGULATION SYSTEMS

All life exists within a thin shell of air, water, and soil called the *biosphere*. The biosphere can be thought of as the parent ecosystem or life support system. It furnishes the water and oxygen needed by all ecosystems on every continent.

The biosphere is composed of thousands of ecosystems which display countless combinations of different climates, vegetation, and animals. It is a mysterious reality that the systems and subsystems in the biosphere operate in concert with each other as a balanced and self-regulated whole. Winter in the northern hemisphere is balanced by summer in the southern hemisphere; the proportion of seawater to freshwater remains relatively constant; and the composition of the air remains stable.

For a glimpse into one self-regulating system, let us examine the amount of freshwater on earth. Although we can calculate the amount of water in a liquid state on our planet, such a statistic can be misleading. The earth's water is constantly moving, taking chemicals into solution and leaving them behind, turning from vapor to liquid to snow to ice, joining a glacier for thousands of years, or flowing up through the roots of plants in unknown metabolic processes that use hydrogen and exhale oxygen.

Water evaporating into the air begins a lengthy series of processes that all contribute to regulating the amount of water on earth. When the sun shines on a water surface, it causes evaporation; the water rises and clouds are formed, which the wind blows toward land. Particles of dust combine with the moisture in the clouds, and eventually a mountain range on the ground below or convection currents within the clouds force the particles to fall in some form of precipitation. As soon as the clouds are dissipated, the sun begins forming more clouds.

This natural system not only regulates the amount of freshwater being carried from the oceans to the land masses, but also controls the global temperature. As temperature rises from the impact of solar energy, there is an increasing rate of evaporation and cloud

3
_____

Water cycle

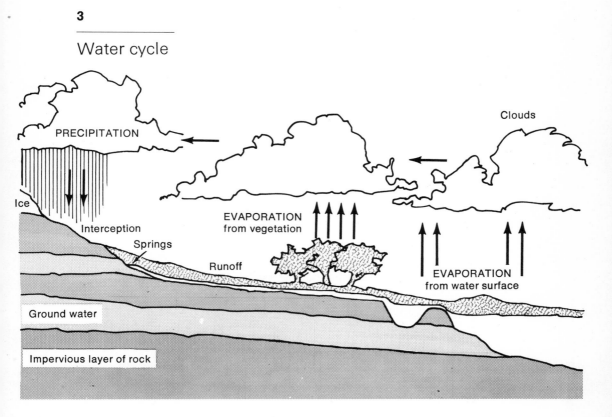

formation. With greater cloud cover there is greater reflection of the sun's rays, as well as less absorption of the sun's heat by the earth's surface. As the temperature and barometric pressure change, the moisture in the clouds is condensed into precipitation, the clouds dissipate and the sunshine begins the cycle again. This self-regulating system guarantees that living organisms will have an adequate amount of water and a constant temperature range. It is only one in an endless series of mutually dependent, self-regulating processes.

ENERGY FLOW

The key to both temperature and the amount of available water is, of course, the sun. The sun is the source of all energy. It is the force that activates diverse processes throughout the biosphere. The problem, however, is that, like everything else we need, there is only a limited amount of sunshine. The earth has an energy budget: only so much is available each day, or throughout each succession of seasons. One immediately obvious consequence of this fact is that only a certain amount of activity can be supported by the daily pulse of solar energy. A limited and finite amount of energy is available from the sun, and there is no other source of energy available to us.

Figure 4 illustrates how solar energy flows through the biosphere. Note that all of the energy reaching the earth from the sun eventually leaves the earth. Some sunshine flows through our planetary household very rapidly, and some stays here quite a while. The solar energy that one afternoon warms a rock or a sidewalk and is lost to the depths of space the next night passes through very quickly. The solar energy that grows a tree, which is logged and then processed into paper that is in turn left as litter to decay in our gutters and sewers, passes through the earth's system a little more slowly. The energy that grew the trees that are today the coal piles being used to make steel passed through very slowly.

The earth radiates enough heat out into space nightly so that the sun does not heat the earth's surface a little more each day until everything wilts and dies; yet the earth retains enough solar energy to support all living things. New research indicates that this regulation of global temperatures within a critically small range is related to the amount of carbon dioxide (CO_2) in the atmosphere. Small disruptions in the makeup of the thin layer of atmosphere surrounding the earth could cause serious consequences. Professor Kenneth E. F. Watt, an ecologist at the University of California

Solar energy utilization

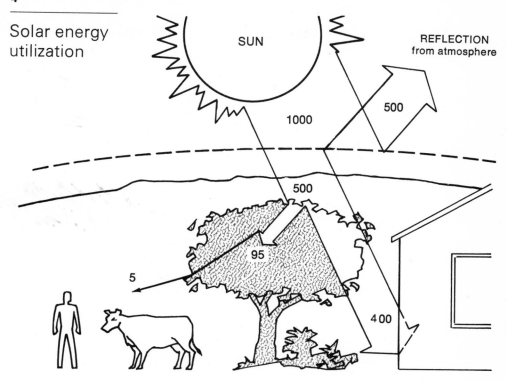

This illustration represents the fact that of every 1000 units of solar energy that reaches the biosphere, only half (500 units) reaches the earth's surface. Of these, 400 units are used immediately as heat. Of the remaining 100 units, 95 are used for plant respiration, leaving only 5 units to be incorporated into food.

(Davis), warns that mankind is polluting the air so universally with industrial and automobile wastes, and possibly with smoke and water vapor from the supersonic transport, that enough of the sun's rays may be blotted out to cause a temperature drop leading to another ice age. If such an epoch reoccurs, half of North America and much of the other continents will be covered by ice. The technological alternatives available to man under such conditions of cataclysmic change have been much discussed in the realm of science fiction, and hopefully they will remain there. Other ecologists are warning us that the CO_2 from the increasing use of fossil fuels will cause the planet to warm up several degrees. This could lead to a rise of 400 feet in the ocean's level.

There are other problems of energy use that cause immediate concern. The sunshine of billions of years ago was transformed by plant life and then further transformed by geologic processes into petroleum, natural gas, and coal, the so-called fossil fuels. Only so much solar energy was available to those ancient and now extinct plants; therefore, the amount of fossil fuels now available to us is limited. We take these fuels for granted and have become dependent on them. Imagine trying to function without drawing upon these energy reserves! What is going to happen in the near future when we run out of large, relatively inexpensive supplies of oil and natural gas?

Atomic energy has been proposed as an alternative energy source, but it does not solve the basic energy inequity. Both fission and fusion materials are as finite as fossil fuels. There are a few additional problems that must be considered. The first is the experimental nature of atomic energy plants. During 1969 and 1970 many were closed for repairs, and several serious accidents have taken place. Almost all facilities under construction now are behind schedule because of fabrication problems. We simply have not taken the time for an adequate development program.

The second serious disadvantage to consider is the generation and handling of the waste products from nuclear power plants. The very nature of the plants today insures a low level of fuel utilization. Many gallons and pounds of radioactive waste material from nuclear reactors now sit in permanent storage. A safe way of disposing of them has not yet been found, and they keep accumulating in various barbed-wire-enclosed "dumps" scattered throughout the world. Radioactive wastes have also been encased in relatively fragile containers and dumped into the ocean.

Several scientists involved with nuclear research have expressed alarm about genetic damage from atomic radiation. While their warnings have focused on human damage, all forms of life are jeopardized. We simply are not sure what constitutes a safe dose of radiation or what an unreasonable risk is. While exposure can be monitored accurately in laboratory tests, those conditions do not exist in a mobile society.

Another drawback is the heat pollution, which would occur on a massive scale if the switch were made from fossil fuels to nuclear energy. Most of this heat pollution would be of the most serious kind, increasing the temperature of water by using it to cool the reactors and generate steam. Warm water contains less oxygen for fish and causes changes in the marine plant life of that area. It is

12

possible to upset the earth's marine ecosystems and weather patterns with the resulting thermal pollution.

On the other hand, if the cooling water needed by nuclear power plants is cooled before reuse by being sent through convection towers, the heat will be passed on to the air. A consistent rise in air temperature could modify a region's climate, possibly contribute to upsetting the self-regulating system that maintains the narrow temperature range permitting life to exist.

We may find solutions to these problems, but right now the appealing goal of universal and inexhaustible atomic energy is both difficult and distant.

FOOD CHAINS

The small portion of solar energy that green plants use for their own growth is the basic fuel for all life. The other major ingredients of plant material—water, carbon dioxide, oxygen, and minerals from the soil—are all available within the living "household," but they require the presence of sunshine before they can combine to form plant life. Food, then, is an edible combination of solar energy and nutrients. The energy stored in plant material may be utilized by several different animals, but eventually all energy leaves the household as radiant heat.

For instance, the solar energy in grass eaten by a rabbit who is later eaten by a predator is finally given off as heat through respiration as the predator hunts. But only a small portion of the solar energy in all the grass the rabbit ever ate is available to the predator that eats him. The rabbit has used most of that energy in his metabolic processes while scurrying about eating, avoiding earlier predators, digging his home, and going about other activities.

A food chain forms when basic plant food is consumed by animals, and these plant eaters (herbivores) are consumed by larger and larger carnivores. Several square miles of grassland may support large communities of rabbits, moles, herbivorous birds and mice, or a small herd of cattle, but all of these plant-eating animals will only support a few hawks, a fox or two, or one man. The idea of a food chain functioning so that one organism is dependent on a few lesser organisms in a progressive chain may be misleadingly simple. Such a peak is only identifiable within a web of feeding relationships. It is useful to graph food pyramids because they combine feeding relationships with energy flow through the ecosystem. (See Figures 5 and 6.)

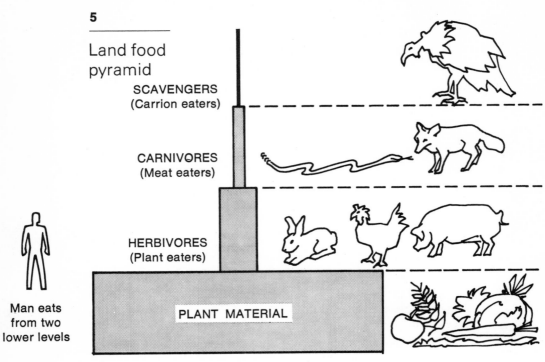

Land food pyramid

SCAVENGERS
(Carrion eaters)

CARNIVORES
(Meat eaters)

HERBIVORES
(Plant eaters)

PLANT MATERIAL

Man eats
from two
lower levels

In this diagram the blocks represent the energy available from the same mass of food at each level.

A higher percentage of the sun's energy is available to plant-eaters than to those who feed on the animals who have consumed the plant-eaters. For instance, it takes fifty pounds of plant food (corn or maize) to produce one pound of beef. Man can eat either corn or beef, but while an acre of corn can feed 1,000 men for one day, if the corn were fed to cattle, and then men ate the meat, that acre would feed only 50 men for one day.

We can eat greens, wheat, nuts, fish, and fruits, as well as meat, and therefore we can manage to sustain ourselves in a wide variety of local environments. In an area where some choice exists between eating the plants or the plant-eaters, population pressures can be adjusted temporarily by moving down the food chain toward basic plant food. We may be observing this kind of adjustment in the United States, Western Europe and other countries that consume large quantities of meat. As the price of meat increases drastically, families will look to less expensive substitutes that provide just as much energy as steaks and roasts.

6

Ocean food pyramid

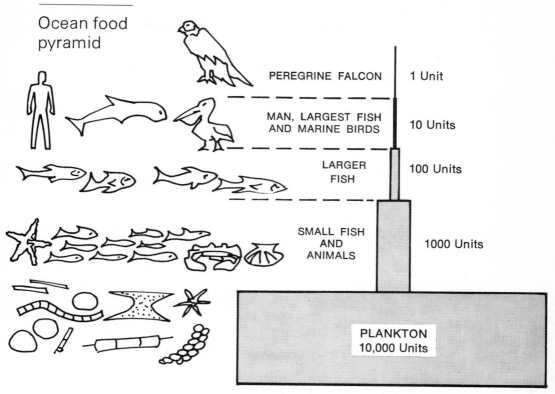

PEREGRINE FALCON	1 Unit
MAN, LARGEST FISH AND MARINE BIRDS	10 Units
LARGER FISH	100 Units
SMALL FISH AND ANIMALS	1000 Units
PLANKTON 10,000 Units	

This diagram illustrates the fact that there is a 90% reduction in energy available in each succeeding level. For example it takes 1000 pounds of small fish to produce 100 pounds of larger fish.

As populations increase rapidly, a person can recognize the problems of producing increasingly large supplies of meat on land for which there are many other demands. The old law of physics that states that no two things can occupy exactly the same place at exactly the same time still applies. People cannot live or produce essential manufactured goods on the same space that is being used for growing food. If more people can be fed by eating plants than by eating the plant-eaters, then meat-eating populations will find reasons for switching. That solution will not last very long, considering the time that it currently takes for populations to double; and it certainly offers no alternatives to societies that long long ago were forced to give up eating meat in any significant quantity.

To understand better the relationship between energy flow and food chains, consider the following: One of the universal problems of human communities is how to lift water from canals and streams onto croplands. The most economical way (at the least cost to local residents) is to construct a waterwheel that will be turned by the river's current, thereby lifting the water up and dumping it into a flume. A similar device is a wind-driven pump, but unfortunately all areas do not have the current, the wind, or the materials available for such structures. Perhaps one ox could be harnessed to a simple water elevator. His cost to the local system would be the land on which to grow his feed and the human energy to care for him. Alternatively, several people could perhaps turn the pump, but much of the water raised would go for food necessary to sustain them. They could eat grazing animals but this would require a large herd of animals, as well as a large parcel of grazing land and more human labor to care for them.

Technology and modern economic systems have given us another alternative—selling some of the crops or grazing animals for cash to buy an engine and gasoline. Use of fossil fuel enables a farmer to trade a portion of the harvest from a few months of sunshine for a large amount of irrigation water. The system that depends on yesterday's sunshine—gasoline—is operating with an energy deficit; that is, more energy is being put into the farming of that cropland than the resulting food provides. This imbalance does not appear as a high cost to the local system because that reality is not part of the price of gasoline. Another real danger exists, in that the community may become totally dependent on the availability of gasoline. Such a dependency is very unrealistic because the supply of fossil fuels is finite.

If, to expand the population, people use an energy source that is limited, and therefore available only temporarily, they will be forced to change their style of life drastically when that source of energy is no longer available. In this example, when gasoline is no longer available for the pump, many people or a few animals will have to man the pump, or the community will have to find a new power source. This rapid adjustment will require many changes in the social organization of that area. Imagine having to change a fundamentally important part of your life style by tomorrow morning—for example, to suddenly wake up and find yourself without automobiles or electricity.

16

Levels of organization

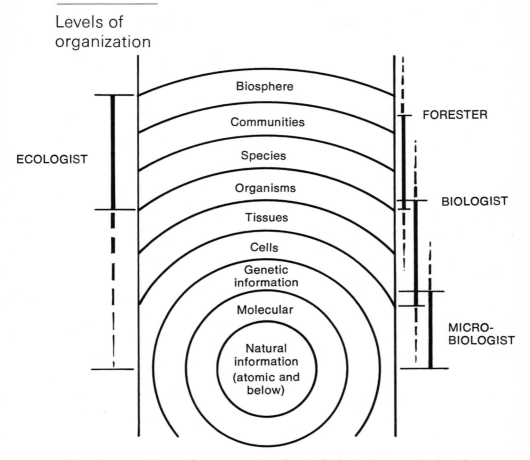

This diagram shows the various levels of biological organization in ascending order of complexity. The range of study of these various levels is shown for several specialists. The heavier part of the vertical bar indicates levels given greatest emphasis.

LEVELS OF ORGANIZATION

"Social organization" refers to the relationships of individuals and institutions in any group. What that group is and how it functions depends on many different relationships. At the elemental level, we must consider that all life is composed of atoms. However, an organism is more than a group of atoms of the right kind and quantity. What a living thing is depends on a plan of organization known as genetic information. This information includes not only detailed plans for the organism's structure—amoeba or zebra—but also information about its daily activities. Such information determines the characteristics of that population (lives in dead logs, is active at night, bites people), the community's role in the ecosystem (dependent on whom? necessary for what?); and the participation of that system in the total affairs of the biosphere (that is, does it threaten the existence of the other systems or the energy balance?).

At another level of consideration is the fact that genetic information interacts with natural information further to affect the behavior of organisms. Natural information includes the principle that atoms can join only in certain combinations to form a limited number of molecules. Oxygen joins readily with carbon and nitrogen but cannot combine with neon or helium. Such things are controlled by the natural properties of the chemical elements, which are the result of the unknown origin of matter. Natural information also includes climatic conditions, seasonal variations, and the force of gravity.

Figure 7 notes that, starting with the most universal type of organization (in the center), and working outward toward increasingly specialized examples, each level of organization is the result of the genetic and natural units from the levels below it. The two types of information affect the organism in varying proportions, but all of the genetic and all of the natural information are utilized at the next level or organization.

All information is essential. For instance, imagine an ecologist investigating the chances of survival for the California brown pelican in an area of the ocean next to a heavily polluted port or harbor. While he is primarily concerned with all of the external phenomena that surround and affect the species within their ecosystem, the ecologist must also know enough about the bird's internal processes to ascertain which chemicals will damage the bird's fertility. The organs and the various internal systems are made up of tissues that are in turn made up of cells, all of which have properties that must be considered by the ecologist.

BIOGEOCHEMICAL CYCLES

To make the ecologist's job even more complex, additional data must be considered. The term *biogeochemical* denotes natural cycles that include biological, geological, and chemical factors. These cycles facilitate all the self-regulating processes of the life support system by providing fresh air and transforming "dead" organic material into a form that can be taken back into a plant's metabolic system. For instance, the fox and the rabbit population will return to the soil and nourish the grass and trees of their habitat. As bacteria break down the dead animal's tissues into a molecular level of organization, the last bits of solar energy from the grass eaten directly or indirectly by the animal are given off into space as latent heat. A carcass seems to disappear, but it actually sinks into the ground in a rain of molecules and flows into the air as gases. Water percolating through the soil (using solar energy to get it there and gravity to pull it through) is passed upward through plant roots to start another life phase in a continuous process of circulation.

All of the biogeochemical cycles deal with molecular recombinations in diverse chemical reactions. These reactions occur in the soil, some in the atmosphere, some in lakes and oceans, and some within various organisms. All self-regulating cycles include at least

8

Carbon-oxygen cycles

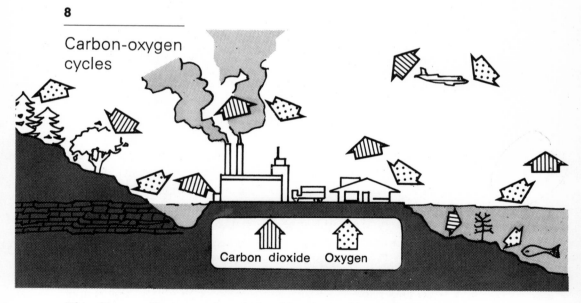

This diagram illustrates the relationship of two biogeochemical cycles. Carbon and oxygen. The atmosphere and bodies of water serve as reservoirs of carbon dioxide and oxygen. Carbon dioxide is produced by animal respiration, burning fuels, dissolving carbonates, and consumed by plants in photosynthesis. Oxygen is produced in significant amounts only by green plants during photosynthesis. It is consumed by animals during respiration and by the combustion of fuels.

9

Nitrogen cycle

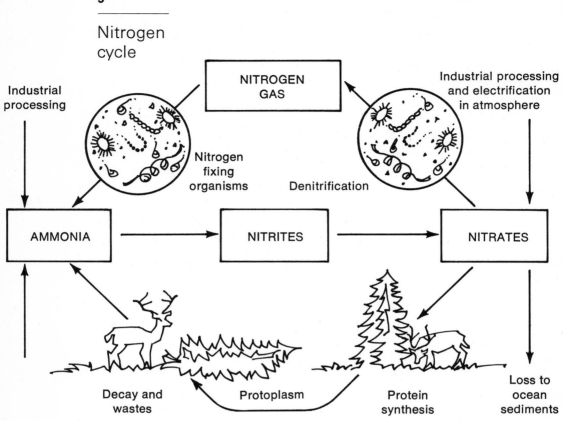

two of these reaction sites; and at least one, the nitrogen cycle, encompasses all four sites (air, soil, water, and organisms). Several of the more prominent cycles are illustrated in figures 8 and 9. As they all involve the atmosphere as a common medium, they overlap considerably. The atmosphere is not a static body of fixed proportions but a holding area for many molecules needed for a variety of processes. The atmosphere is constantly accepting and giving up particles and gases that facilitate the life process. Many intricate and little understood self-regulating systems maintain the proper combination of carbon dioxide, oxygen, and nitrogen, so that both animals and plants are sustained by the same medium, even though the waste product of one is the life blood of the other.

Although we would have no cycles without life and no life without cycles, we would have *neither* without solar energy. All life is paced by the earth's daily ration of sunshine.

EVOLUTION

The total of land, water and air, self-regulating systems, levels of organization, energy flow, food chains, and biogeochemical cycles do not create the stir that the term *evolution* does. Yet evolution is nothing more than all these processes interacting over a long period of time. The term *evolution* has taken on a cultural meaning that has little to do with its biological definition. The word *evolution* means a natural process of change in response to the physical changes of an aging planet. This process of change is neither good nor bad. Given a planet of the earth's composition and position relative to the sun, the changes we can observe in the fossil record are natural. We know that when the earth was first in orbit around the sun, there was very little oxygen in its atmosphere. As the first, primitive, drifting marine organisms gave off oxygen through the photosynthetic process, new conditions were created, promoting evolutionary change. Oxygen and ozone shielded the earth's surface from deadly ultraviolet radiation. Now the land could be colonized by life from the sea. Conditions change and species change.

Why is the earth where it is? Where did the material originally come from? Nature is more complicated than we can imagine, and there are many more theories that attempt to explain the processes of nature. Dr. Albert Einstein had faith in man's ability someday to understand these questions scientifically. Yet Einstein described himself as a very religious man.

Evolution remained unknown to man for thousands of years because the processes of change unfolded so slowly. Not even in several human lifetimes could a difference be detected in a large organism's appearance or behavior. Such changes finally became evident only after the development of natural history, initiated by Aristotle's collecting and early attempts at classification, and the availability of a very precise written language. Only then could observers have a remote chance of noticing and describing evolutionary change.

In 1835, Charles Darwin happened to travel to a group of islands, the Galapagos, 400 miles off the coast of Ecuador, where he noticed variations in the beaks of one kind of finch from the mainland. He realized that a single species of finch from the mainland had colonized the islands and, through a process he called "natural selection," now expressed itself in several species with highly specialized eating habits. (See Figure 10.) One fed exclusively on insects, some ate fruit and berries, another ate hard-shelled seeds, and another utilized sticks to poke into cracks in search of larvae and insects. Their beaks had become quite different as a result of their developing different eating habits and the natural selection of the beak most efficient in obtaining the most preferred or most available food.

From his observations in the Galapagos and elsewhere, Charles Darwin put forth three main points which still form the foundation of our understanding about the dynamics of evolution.

1. Organisms tend to reproduce beyond their capacity for survival. We have seen examples of this in the number of cones a pine tree sheds or in the huge "tadpole" populations in creeks and ponds that are never seen later as hordes of frogs.

2. Organisms tend to vary slightly from one another in many ways. This is true of behavior and internal chemistry as well as of external appearance or the shape of the skeleton. We now understand that these differences can be of inherited genetic origin as well as isolated mutations. The evolutionary process involves repeated thinnings of large numbers of offspring that contain slight differences.

3. Those organisms that survive are "the best fitted to cope with the environment." "Survival" is dependent upon the relationship between the organism's characteristics and the properties of the envioronment; "to cope with" means to live at least to reproductive maturity and to mate successfully.

The most famous example of how such thinnings select for "the best fitted to cope with the environment" is that of the peppered moth in England. As soot from developing industry darkened the various surfaces—trees, walls, and the like—that these moths might light upon, the white variety became more conspicuous to bird predators and the brown variety became less so. The pressure of bird predators was shifted totally to the white moth, as dark coloring came to have increased survival value.

This example brings us to the core of evolutionary change: The peppered moth *phenotype* (its total amount of genetic information) included a white and a brown coloring scheme. That unit of organizational information known as "peppered moth" would have been in danger of becoming extinct if its continuity were dependent on

Galapagos
finches

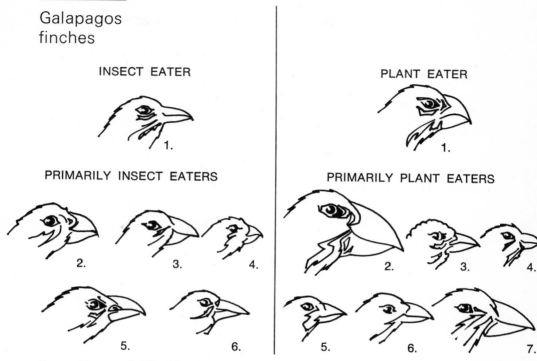

INSECT EATER

1.

PLANT EATER

1.

PRIMARILY INSECT EATERS

2.   3.   4.

5.   6.

PRIMARILY PLANT EATERS

2.   3.   4.

5.   6.   7.

Insect Eaters: *1. Warbler finch. 2, 3, 4, Large, medium and small tree finch. 5. Tool-using finch. 6. Mangrove finch.*

Plant Eaters: *1. Vegetarian tree-finch. 2, 3, 4, Large, medium and small ground finch. 5. Sharp-beaked finch. 6. Cactus ground finch. 7. Large cactus ground finch.*

the "white package" alone. The survival of the peppered moth in a rapidly changing environment was assured when the genotype calling for white coloration was not allowed to reproduce, and the brown variety was favored by "natural" conditions.

Modern research has added many more details to Darwin's original contribution. We are learning now how some animals "control" their own populations. For example, some marine birds have come to utilize only a certain portion of a certain rocky shore as nesting sites, even though hundreds of miles of similar shores are all around them. Many birds who do not have a nesting site watch those who do from nearby rocks. These adults appear to be in reserve and can breed the following year to maintain a minimum population. If nesting sites are restricted, births are limited so that the food source, fish, is not threatened with serious depletion. This principle of a species indirectly protecting its own survival, by limiting the pressure on its food source through expression of territoriality, has parallels among animals and land-based birds.

This territorial behavior has been interpreted by some zoologists and naturalists as a self-seeking trait. Recent studies, however, indicate that it should be considered as behavior that has survival value through controlling population density. When populations whose members express territoriality increase their members, some are forced to the fringes of the habitat where it is much more difficult to find food and shelter. The mortality rate is higher there, and population growth is controlled without damaging the food supply within the habitat.

CHAPTER TWO

Major
Ecosystems
of the
Biosphere

We easily recognize the different appearances of ecosystems such as deserts, oceans, and forests; but all of these areas share a very important ecological principle. Each of them tends to evolve until the greatest possible variety and quantity of plants and animals are established. The rate of change is very fast early in this process (called succession), and the rate diminishes as the final stage—climax—of succession is approached.

As an illustration of succession, let us observe an island that has recently been created by volcanic eruption. For a brief instant the island is bare of all living organisms. Then colonization starts. From the sea and air: airborne algae, microscopic spores of mosses and ferns; seaborne seeds floating ashore on debris or surrounded by "saltwaterproof" shells. Scavenging birds bring additional seeds in their digestive tracts and drop them ashore with a ready supply of fertilizer; other seeds and minute animals cling to bird feathers and feet. Animals arrive swimming, floating on debris, or as eggs. Hundreds of organisms become established and bound together by a web of complex relations.

The community of plants and animals becomes a fascinating interplay of biological, physical, and historical forces. Various members feed upon or feed others, and all must make large or small adjustments to each other and to their physical surroundings.

During each of the successive stages through which an island community passes, there is change in most, if not all, of the organisms that make it up. New plants and animals appear, and their arrival brings about changes that may make survival more difficult for some of the old organisms, but easier for other ones. This process of continual development gradually slows down until the life process is concerned primarily with maintenance of existing populations. Such a period is characterized by large mature trees and an open forest floor. It was in such an area in the vicinity of Yellowstone Park that Lewis and Clark faced starvation. This is because the climax forest offered little browse for deer and other animals. Since that time, forest fires and other forces have reinitiated succession and animal populations have increased.

Man has in fact intruded into the natural succession of many ecosystems. By clearing forests, through intensive one-crop agriculture, and by the massive harvesting of whales, seals, passenger pigeons, and buffalo, man has upset the delicate relationships that move a natural community toward a climax stage. Man no longer functions as part of a community, but by and large he attempts to conquer or control nature. By recklessly spreading poisons across the world's ecosystems, by placing bounties upon the heads of certain predatory mammals and birds, and by attempting to manage communities so that they will produce the maximum amount of meat or plant material, man may be defeating himself. Each ecosystem is a complex and delicate mechanism, and by his ignorant and often destructive behavior the species *homo sapiens* may be committing suicide slowly.

The major consequence of succession is the fact that the ecosystem will prevail in the face of natural disaster, but that man-created communities and systems cannot exist without constant intervention. For example, imagine a wheat farm and an adjoining wild meadow both subjected to a heavy frost or the invasion of insects. The wheat field would be wiped out by the frost or the insects, while the meadow would show a few brown spots from the frost but be protected from complete destruction by insect predation by the insects' natural enemies—other insects or birds. A natural community could never exist with merely one variety of plant or animal like that in a farm field. Acres and acres of wheat represent an open invitation to all wheat-eaters for a gourmet treat. The farmer can only respond with additional "unnatural" behavior: chemical pesticides.

A natural community evolves in such a fashion that a balance exists between all organisms. Insects that eat certain varieties of grass are controlled by other insects—possibly lacewings or ladybug beetles, or by birds. Most insecticides, however, kill all insects rather than the one or two we have identified as "pests."

Frost would also have a minimal impact on a natural ecosystem like the meadow, because many varieties of grasses exist in the community, and each has different characteristics. While some may be killed by frost, there are many others that are naturally resistant to low temperatures. Other grasses could survive under conditions of low moisture or fire. It would require a simultaneous onslaught of freeze, fire, flood, and drought to kill the meadow. One bulldozer has a greater impact than if all of these natural phenomena occurred at the same time.

Man is reducing the total life support system of the biosphere by reducing *diversity* within each of the ecosystem types. When a farmer plants 2,000 acres of wheat, he is violating a fundamental ecological principle. He has replaced with one variety of one plant many varieties of organisms that have developed a system of interdependence and interrelationships over a period of time. The farmer must now maintain his artificial system by plowing it, seeding it, watering it, harvesting it and attempting to maintain its fertility. The natural ecosystem did all of these operations by itself.

It may now be obvious that the farmer is decreasing the stability of that portion of the biosphere's life support system by reducing the diversity of organisms. An examination of the earth's major ecosystems shows increasing evidence of man's impact on the natural succession of organisms. In every case—oceans, rivers, lakes, deserts, tundras—the large ecosystems have been diverted from a natural balance of organisms to a state of disruption that threatens the continued supply of fresh air, clean water, and nutritious food.

An examination of man's impact on some of the major ecosystems will explain a few of the consequences of intervention and what the future offers if the disruption of natural succession continues at its present rate.

For instance, because some trees are more valuable than others, and so are logged commercially, they may never be established as a climax forest. Such a practice will upset the interdependent relationships among the natural successions of bird, insect, and animal populations.

There are many possibilities that must be explored in terms of interdependence. Does man's intervention in the natural succession of other organisms have any effect on man? Does intervention help man achieve a better and more stable environment for himself? These are judgments that must be made after intensive research.

Casual or thoughtless intrusion into the interdependent relationships among the various animal and plant communities may have serious and unanticipated repercussions.

OCEANS

Because the seas of the world cover almost three-fourths of the earth's surface and extend to great depths, marine ecosystems are the most extensive and diverse in the biosphere. The controlling factor for these systems is a thin zone at the surface of the water known as the photaic zone. Here enough sunlight penetrates the sea water to power photosynthesis. Even though the oceans are extensive, the basic food source is available only along the edges of continental land masses. The phytoplankton that grow in these areas are nourished by food nutrients washing off the mainland. In some cases, as off the coast of Peru, an upwelling ocean current continually raises these nutrients to the organisms in the photaic zone. These phytoplankton are the basic food for all marine creatures. The oceans moderate temperatures and climates the world over. The amounts of carbon dioxide, oxygen, and nitrogen in the atmosphere are regulated by marine oxygen production and by the storage of CO_2 and nitrogen in the oceans.

The oceans are often used now as a dump for many of our wastes. The relatively long food chains there bring about the concentration of chemicals, like DDT, and radioactive particles until some seafood is unsafe to eat. Hard pesticides, for instance, do not dissolve or break down for many years under natural conditions, and they run off in suspension from irrigation ditches to streams, rivers, and eventually to the ocean. Winds also carry particles great distances. Traces of pesticides have been found in both the Arctic and Antarctic oceans. Microscopic amounts of these chemicals enter the phytoplankton; small fish eat the phytoplankton and also consume the pesticide. The chemical structure of DDT prevents its passing as normal wastes, and so the DDT in the phytoplankton eaten by the fish accumulates in its body. By the time the DDT has passed through the ocean food chains to larger fish, the third or fourth reconcentration has been completed. All the DDT concentrated in the foods eaten by man (or by any other predator) accumulates to a grand and possibly dangerous total. This buildup begins to impair our organism's basic internal chemistry. Many disruptions may occur before the fatal one, but we are already observing the failure of marine birds to reproduce.

SEASHORES AND ESTUARIES

Areas where the tides are rising and falling on mud flats, rocks, bluffs, dunes, or in tidal pools, and where freshwater mixes with saltwater, form an especially fertile spectrum of ecosystems. These areas are not to be regarded merely as a transition between land and sea, but as truly unique areas with very special properties. Tidal action is an additional energy input that many plants and animals need in order to gain nutrients. A great variety of food producers, plus the shallowness of the water, mean that the food consumers are close at hand. Little energy is lost in gathering food. Therefore, these are uniquely fertile areas.

Far too often these shallow tidal areas are used as dumps by factories and municipalities. And signs like: *No Swimming, No Fishing Due to Contamination,* and *Clams Unhealthy to Eat* are common near seashores and estuaries. Frequently towns and cities pipe raw sewage into the nearest body of saltwater as a convenient and inexpensive means of disposal.

Several electric generating plants using nuclear energy or fossil fuel have been installed in these areas. Large volumes of warm water enter the estuaries and reduce the amount of oxygen (O_2), in solution. This ruins the habitat for fish, allowing the rapid growth of algae. Diversity and balance are replaced with a population explosion of one species (algae) and a destroyed ecosystem.

Large mud flats are being dredged to facilitate shipping and are being filled for industry. This deprives the estuary of total communities of organisms and further reduces diversity.

RIVERS

Rivers define the watersheds that supply us with water for drinking, irrigation, and industry. If soils are not drained properly, plant growth is not possible. Free-flowing streams and rivers drain all land areas and return water to the oceans where it is subsequently lifted into the air through evaporation and returned to the land. Our rivers and streams are not only the actual habitat for fish and insects but are an essential part of many other habitats. Animals, birds, and snakes all drink from these watercourses, and their survival depends upon a supply of clean water.

We presently use rivers as channels of transportation, to distribute irrigation water, to generate electricity, and to dispose of wastes. One official has even suggested rivers are valuable natural sewers.

As rivers are increasingly used to satisfy man's needs, they fail in their ability to service the various pre-existing habitats. An example of a badly deteriorated river system is the industrial area around the Great Lakes. The Cuyahoga River in Cleveland eventually became so filled with oily wastes and sludge that it burst into flame spontaneously, destroying bridges, wharves, and warehouses.

LAKES

Most lakes now in existence date from the last ice age, and all are changing at a rate inversely proportional to their size. This is because they are slowly being filled with sediments from the area they drain. In the rainy season a lake acts as a settling basin, and tons of new material are deposited on its floor. An alpine lake bordered by an extensive meadow is actually only a remnant of a larger lake.

There are commonly three zones of life in lakes: the area along the shore where rooted vegetation grows, an open surface area where plankton live, and a deep water zone where no basic food is produced. In temperate regions, lakes become stratified according to water temperature. This is layering by differential heating and cooling. In the summertime a warm body of water a few feet deep lies over a distinctly colder layer. In the winter the reverse is true. When the layers reverse in the early summer a bloom (population increase) of algae often occurs because of the mixing of nutrients and oxygen.

Lakes and ponds are the ecosystems most easily constructed by man. They are made at great monetary cost; they sometimes inundate croplands and more natural ecosystems not easily constructed by man. But their immediate value in flood control is high, and we continue to build them. Reservoirs, like lakes, act as giant settling basins. Ultimately, they too become meadows. The useful life of most of the dams now being built is one hundred years, the time required for silt to fill the reservoirs they create.

Siltation (the depositing of layers of silt) in lakes and reservoirs is only one of the problems we have to worry about. These bodies of water also age in relation to water quality. Nutrients in the form of dead leaves and grass are being washed into them along with chemical fertilizers. All these nutrients together provide an unnatural abundance of food for algae, which bloom profusely, exhausting the water's oxygen and killing the fish. The water turns from clear to a murky light green and is no longer fit for recreational or commercial fishing. This deterioration occurs even more quickly if industrial wastes are allowed to flow into a lake. Lake Erie has actually been killed by combinations of unwise practices.

FRESHWATER MARSHES

This type of ecosystem has been vilified and eliminated wherever possible. A marsh seemed, for a long time, to be only an unhealthy sort of place and a waste of good land. We now understand that these marshes are among the more important self-regulating systems. They are reservoirs maintaining a certain level of ground water, which is important to prevent saltwater intrusion into a land area, and to provide adequate water through dry months.

These marsh systems are similar to the estuaries in that they are very fertile and host a large variety of life. Rice paddy culture can be looked upon as management of freshwater marshes. Ecologists now know how to manage and control disease-carrying mosquitoes and snails without DDT, and it is no longer necessary to destroy the entire habitat for "health" reasons.

The outstanding example today of the mistreatment of marshes is in the Florida Everglades. Land developers, airports, and large canals are all threatening this area with total destruction. It is ironic that the drainage required for development will allow saltwater to intrude further into the ground water system maintained by the Everglades. Wells in the newly developed areas will go sour, forcing residents either to pipe in water or abandon their communities.

DESERTS

The term *desert* usually refers to amount of rainfall rather than extremes of temperature. Cool deserts exist in eastern areas of the state of Washington, and hot deserts occur in the southwestern United States. Ten inches of annual rainfall is the arbitrary division between deserts and grassland. The Sonora Desert is an interesting exception. Rainfall there is over ten inches annually, but the evaporation rate is extremely high. Lack of rainfall in the deserts is usually caused by a high pressure area or a range of high mountains that block the clouds and prevent moisture from entering the area. Both the plants and animals of these dry areas demonstrate many intricate and exotic mechanisms for survival. Water conservation is the universal problem. Many plants only grow when there is water.

An unseasonal rain results in a sudden flowering of the desert floor and this vegetative material soon returns to the soil where seeds are waiting for the next wet year.

Some desert animals never drink water, and they have many unique metabolic features to reduce their moisture requirements. Some plants actually manufacture chemicals that prevent too many plants from growing in one area. These chemicals enter the soil from decaying plant parts and in a gaseous form that prevents competition for water that would endanger the total population. Widely spaced plants with bare soil between them are a common sight in southwestern deserts. This is apparently a natural population control device similar in effect to the "territoriality" of some marine birds mentioned earlier.

Man has divided feelings when it comes to deserts. On one hand he regards them as wastelands, while on the other hand he believes "Just bring water and they will grow us anything." This attitude is even more remarkable when we realize that many of today's deserts are the result of man's agricultural practices. Those practices included importing irrigation water for crops. The increased amount of evaporation allowed salt residues to build up until the soil lost its fertility. This same process is going on today in the southwest and in portions of the central valley of California.

Desert areas are unusual in that they are very slow to recover from intrusions by man or other forces. For instance, it is estimated that an acre stripped of vegetation in the Anza-Borrego Desert (east of San Diego) will take three hundred years to recover. Such stripping only takes a moment, as when a dune buggy churns up a slope. Little water is available for the movement of minerals and nutrients, or for the metabolic processes necessary for plant growth in this desert.

GRASSLANDS

Large interior sections of all the continents are grasslands, including about one-third of North America. The grasses range from tall varieties (five to eight feet) to short grasses of only a few inches. Sometimes these grasslands are marked by isolated trees and shrubs or a continuous line of trees along a watercourse. Grassland with infrequent trees is called a savannah.

Usually several species of grass are present in a grassland, and some grow only late in the season, thus stretching production beyond the moisture peak. The dominant species will account for as much as seventy per cent of the grass present, but many other species will be present in small numbers; these can easily become the dominant if climatic or grazing conditions change.

The dust bowl of the 1930's in Oklahoma and Texas was the result of farmers' attempts to obtain an unnatural amount of production from a relatively dry area. Wheat was not meant to be grown in such marginal areas, and a few dry years brought disaster to the area. Much dry farming continues, but we are now making wiser decisions about how to use the grasslands.

These areas have two basic types of grazers, those that burrow under the ground and those that travel on the surface in herds. Plant material is as plentiful below ground as above. The grazers that burrow underground turn the soil naturally and let air reach down into the deep topsoil. We have substituted cattle for the natural grazers, and many ecologists feel that we should re-establish native populations and harvest them on a sustained yield basis. They look forward to the day of buffalo burgers and antelope steak as one way of maintaining an ecological balance.

TUNDRA

Between the forests of Siberia and Canada and the polar ice cap, there is a narrow band of land known as arctic tundra. A similar area, known as alpine tundra, is found above the tree line on the earth's mountain ranges. Contrasted with the deserts, which have limited water, the tundra has very limited heat. It can be described as a frozen grassland. While the movement of nutrients in desert land is restricted by lack of water, nutrients in the tundra are held immobile in the permafrost. This is the layer of soil that is permamently frozen. The surface layer of soil that thaws and then freezes each winter is only a few inches thick.

Despite these harsh conditions, many species have adapted successfully to the cold. Migatory birds nest in these areas and find ample food for themselves and their young. The larger grazers that can be found there in the short summer, such as musk ox, caribou, and reindeer, are also migratory. Since water expands when it freezes, the winter frost causes the upper layer of soil to buckle and rise in "frost heaves" several feet high. This rise and fall of the surface soil is one of the present problems facing the planners of a 48-inch pipeline to be built across the northern part of Alaska. Present plans call for the oil to be heated so that it will flow easily through the pipeline. This heat may make the frost heaves more violent and thereby rupture the line, because the heat could melt some of the permafrost, so that more than the usual amount of water would freeze and buckle the soil the next winter. The rupture of an oil pipeline with a four-foot diameter would spell total destruction for that part of the tundra. The black soil surface would absorb large amounts of heat, and large areas of the tundra would melt. The streams formed by melting would cause erosion.

Another serious problem may be heavy machines, called "weasels," that create depressions in which water accumulates in the summer months. Water collects heat more readily than soil, extending the layer of soil that melts in summer to a deeper level than normal. This situation leads to greater frost heaves and deeper erosion, which in turn lead to more standing water, and so on. Whatever the end of such a process may be, it certainly will not create a good surface on which to lay down a pipeline hundreds of miles long. While it will take 300 years for the desert to recover from man's actions, we can say that the tundra will never recover from the impact of our oil-drilling activities.

FORESTS

The major function of forests is the regulation of the water supply in the biosphere. The thick ground cover and the many roots of a forest ecosystem release rainwater slowly into surface streams and down into ground water systems. Plant life could not survive if water were only available at sporadic intervals. In the forests, vegetation and soil combine to form a sponge, a reservoir that allows air and water to reach the roots of all plants. Without healthy watersheds, rivers would run dry in the summer, plants would die, and animals would starve.

There are three main types of forest. Just south of the tundra is the forest of low diversity, the *taiga*. It is mostly spruce and fir. Further south, taiga gives way to more diversified *coniferous* forests, depending on local conditions of moisture, elevation, and temperature. These coniferous forests yield in turn to a *deciduous* forest of oaks, maples, and hickories. Diversity of species continues to increase as we move south; many shrubs and plants begin to appear in the coniferous forests. The thickening of vegetation is continuous all the way south to the tropical forest, where many vines and air plants appear.

Man has been abusing the forests for thousands of years. The clearing of land for agriculture, the building of ships, and the gathering of fuel have resulted in the deforestation of much of the northern continents. The entire eastern half of the United States was once an unbroken forest, and the Mediterranean area, including North Africa and the Middle East, once had extensive forests. The deforestation and erosion of these areas document man's long-term inability to function as part of natural succession. We seem to have not learned anything from these early tragedies.

It is ironic that in some ways we have gone from one extreme in forest control to the other; from no management of forest resources to tree farms. "Smokey the bear" is the symbol of forest fire prevention and other timber management programs. It may be true that in the short run ashes cannot be logged, but in the long run, forests without fires are not forests. Ecologists and some foresters now understand fire as a natural part of forest ecosystems. Some pine trees are totally dependent on fire for reproduction. Their cones will not open until heated by a forest fire. The coast redwoods need fire periodically to clean out the shrubs. New trees are only a fraction of an inch tall and do not get enough sunlight to begin growing unless the brush is burned out. The many black scars on the redwoods testify to the normalness of fire in that ecosystem.

We are also preventing floods on some of the streams that pass through large alluvial plains where there are extensive redwood groves. The roots of these trees are very close to the surface and require periodic floods to replace exhausted soil. Preventing all fires and flood in these areas has many advantages for us in our time scale—one human lifetime—but we will not see the disruptions we have caused in the forest's natural sequence of changes.

"But what's all the fuss about?" you may ask. "If we turned all the animals loose, let the fields go untended, emptied the dam, and stopped the flow of fossil fuels, we would all starve." That's true, but the point is that to survive we must learn how to sustain ourselves without destroying the system we are dependent upon. Like it or not, we are the manipulators of the biosphere.

CHAPTER THREE

Four Basic
Impacts

Three and one-half billion people inhale the air surrounding the earth and eat food from its soils. Regardless of how diverse their activities, people have these basic dependencies in common. It makes little difference whether soil is mismanaged in Africa or in Iceland—the result is that the planet becomes less able to support life. Automobiles mix lead into the common air supply *wherever* they are driven. We know of many other examples of pollution and environmental destruction from the reports in our newspapers, magazines and books. These can be broken down and classified as four basic kinds of impacts. After defining them, we will develop a basic frame of reference (Chapter 4). The aim of these final chapters is to help in understanding the present situation and to enable us to decide what actions should be taken.

The basic impacts are consistent with what has been discussed in Chapter 1 about the functioning of a typical ecosystem. The central element is its energy source. The first impact is *energy inequities* the system continues to undergo without running down because materials are recycled by the biogeochemical cycles. The second impact is open cycles. A functioning system could also be hampered in two other ways; either it can be contaminated with poisons, or parts of it can be covered over or cut out. These considerations lead to the four basic impacts:

1. Energy imbalance

2. Open cycles

3. "Household" contamination

4. Surface destruction

ENERGY IMBALANCE

It would be a pleasant experience to be able to put $10 in a savings account and withdraw $1000. An even wilder fantasy would be to imagine perpetuating the situation. Unfortunately, in real life one rarely gets something for nothing. Recall that in Chapter 1 it was pointed out that the process of life on earth is powered by solar radiation. This simple realization leads us to the most insidious of the four basic impacts on our life support system. Mankind in general, and western man in particular, depends on the availability of more energy than is currently being supplied by the sun. We rely on petroleum fuels to plant our crops, harvest them, prepare and deliver food to the stores, bring the food to our homes. The same applies to building our houses, lighting, heating, and cooling them.

This energy inequity is dangerous in three ways. First, as the fossil fuels (petroleum, natural gas, and coal) are consumed, surplus heat is produced and radiated out into space.

Geophysicists are alarmed that we may be in danger of warming the earth's atmosphere enough to upset the self-regulating systems that maintain a constant temperature range in our "household." It is conceivable that these systems have a threshold tolerance and that a slight excess beyond that unknown point may precipitate a rapid, unknown, and unexpected result. Knowledge of such a theoretical threshold without knowledge of a specific tolerance for handling nonsolar heat calls for extreme caution. Such considerations have led Dr. Robert Stebbins of the University of California at Berkeley to predict an inevitable return to muscle power. (Both human and animal labor stem from the utilization of our daily solar energy ration.) Dr. Harrison Brown at the California Institute of Technology (Pasadena) has pointed out that the heating of homes, offices, and plants could be done directly with solar heat. This process would also help reduce the amount of heat unnaturally reflected from man-made surfaces in urban areas.

Rather than merely finding alternate energy sources (such as solar or atomic energy) to meet our present needs, it is likely that we will also have to find ways to lower our present energy needs through technology and social reorganization. Can you see people giving up automobiles, single-family homes, and all their electrical appliances? Hardly. Yet these are alternatives to our present style of life that must be considered as the supply of fossil fuel diminishes.

The second danger is that the combustion of fossils fuels results in tremendous quantities of carbon dioxide (CO_2) being added to

11

Greenhouse effect

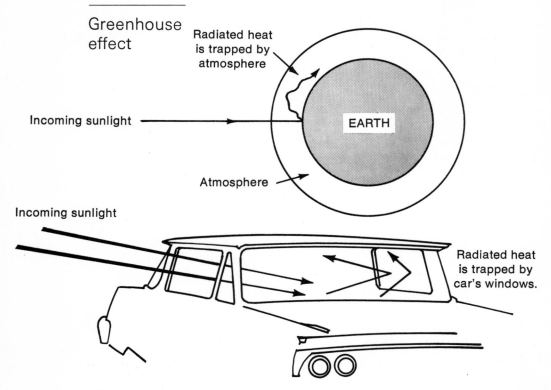

The "greenhouse effect" results when solar energy can enter the bio-sphere easier than it can leave. The portion of CO_2 in the atmosphere has increased about 15%. While this increase has no effect on incoming sunshine, it does retard the passage of infrared (heat) radiation out to space.

Perhaps you have noticed how hot a car interior can become. Sunlight readily enters through the window, warms interior surfaces, which then give off heat. This radiation does not pass through the glass so easily, and is reflected back into the car's interior space. Energy is trapped and warms the inner layer of safety glass until the glass can shatter from the stress. Usually the curved rear window breaks, allowing "the system" to regulate its temperature. Many fear the biosphere might break in a similar way.

the atmosphere. All of the effects of its addition and the subsequent displacement of other gases is not known. On people the effect of additional CO_2 is similar to living at a higher elevation with less oxygen available per breath. It is a richer mixture for plants, as they require carbon dioxide for their metabolism. Aside from the metabolic effects of increases in carbon dioxide, it appears that CO_2 may also restrict or retard the radiation of heat leaving the biosphere. If this is the case, we are creating a "greenhouse effect" by continued use of fossil fuels; that is, as more CO_2 is released into the air, heat is trapped, causing a gradual increase in global temperature.

The third danger of this energy inequity dependence relates to the artificial and temporary life style it may foster. If a human population of a fixed number discovered coal, oil, and gas and switched over to them for as long as they lasted, but did *not* increase their population size, they could probably switch back to forest resources (recent and renewable solar energy) when the fossils fuels were exhausted. However, if the possibilities of fossil fuels were seen as a means to reorganize the society and resulted in increased numbers because "production" could be increased, dependence on a finite resource could be disastrous.

Perhaps it would be a wise plan to utilize the remaining fossil fuels to assist us in transforming our energy dependence back to renewable resources.

OPEN CYCLES

This classification refers both to natural cycles that man has interrupted and to material flows that man could make into a complete, though unnatural, cycle. The outstanding example of the first type would be organic material. In a "natural" situation, leaves, fruit, and nuts will fall to the ground and return to the soil. Man takes many crops from the fields, forests, and sea without returning any organic material to the ground. The wasted organic materials from food harvesting and processing and from kitchen scraps and sewage contain trace mineral elements that are necessary for proper plant growth and human nutrition. Because these elements are not being recycled (returned to the soil), our food is losing its nutritional value, and growing plants are losing their vitality. The U.S. Department of Public Health points out that bread made in 1947 had twice the nutritional value of bread today. The reason is primarily the nature of our culture: expedient merchandising practices allow the wheat germ, the most valuable part of wheat, to be taken off in order to keep insects out of the flour in storage.

The second type of cycle could be represented by the tin can. Supplies of tin and steel ores are finite, yet we do not extend ourselves to preserve these resources. We should close the cycle of

A. Organic material, interrupted natural cycles.

    1) sewage

    2) food-processing scraps

    3) garbage

    4) paper and wood

    5) human skeletons

B. Inorganic material, man-created open cycles.

    1) aluminum cans

    2) tin cans

    3) glass containers

    4) metal objects

buried and "lost" tin cans by gathering them and remaking new containers out of them. (Try to find out who in your community will accept tin or aluminum cans to recycle.)

"HOUSEHOLD" CONTAMINATION

This is more commonly referred to as "pollution," but that term is rather vague and could describe various specific impacts under all of the headings. This impact factor is the most diverse, presenting the very difficult problem of trying to assign a relative value to these varied forms of contamination. That is to say, would it be "better" to have three units of heat and one unit of radiation contamination from a nuclear power plant rather than one unit of heat contamination and six units of chemical contamination (SO_2) from a coal-fired generating plant?

SURFACE OBLITERATION AND DESTRUCTION

This category includes any damage caused by humans to the surface of our life support system (biosphere). Clearing the land to make room for different types of construction projects is a relatively straightforward case of obliteration; such things as logging, open pit mining, tailing dumps, and settlement ponds are also straightforward

Types of "Household" Contamination

A. Chemical

    1) placed in the environment purposely: pesticides, herbicides.

    2) placed in the environment without purpose: flume gases, tire wear, automobile exhausts.

B. Heat

    1) solar heat reflected from man-made surfaces.

    2) heat generated by man at the earth's surface, atomic fission, burning of fossil fuels.

C. Psychological

    1) conflict between the desire for goods and services and the ability to obtain (use) these goods and services.

    2) overstimulation through too many visual, auditory, and other sensory inputs.

    3) cultural stress through an obvious conflict between reality and culturally prescribed behavior.

    4) social stress from population density.

D. Noise

    1) people in crowded areas.

    2) industrial operations.

    3) household activities (dwelling place).

    4) operation of cars, trucks, trains, airplanes.

E. Nonbiodegradable material

    1) plastics

    2) detergents

    3) concrete

    4) glass

F. Radiation

    1) x-ray machines

    2) bomb testing and manufacture

    3) nuclear excavations and gas field activation

    4) nuclear power plants

    5) uranium mine dumps

    6) stored and discarded wastes or by-products

and easy to classify. However, agricultural practices may be considered in several ways and so are difficult to classify. In terms of production on a year-to-year basis, the earth is now producing food of different types, and total production for all forms of life has decreased. In other words, "people food" has displaced animal food: one species displacing many others. Agricultural practices have also increased soil erosion and wind erosion of farmlands. Some soils have been damaged by salination, which results from the evaporation of large quantities of irrigation water, leaving residues in the soil.

Other agricultural areas have seemingly become more fertile because of careful methods. It is possible for a farm to be producing well, but actually losing some topsoil every year. Soils are also damaged by compaction from farm equipment. In most cases these kinds of agricultural impacts depend on local conditions and are not as straightforward as an open pit mine or a parking lot.

Types of Surface Obliteration and Destruction

A. Highways, roads, parking lots, railroads, airports, and all asphalt and concrete surfaces.

B. Surface space for all buildings except greenhouses.

C. Mining activities.

D. Logging activities.

E. Man-precipitated disasters such as mud slides, forest fires, floods.

F. Agricultural impacts.

CHAPTER FOUR

A Basic Frame
of Reference

Research shows that 71% of all smog in U.S. urban communities is caused by the internal combustion engine. Maps of Los Angeles show that two-thirds of the city is either roadway or parking lot. Children in Los Angeles schools are not able to exercise when the smog level reaches a certain point. The people of Los Angeles don't like smog, but apparently they do not see an alternative to driving. Politicians everywhere consider rapid transit from a political point of view (getting re-elected), while the business community considers it from a financial point of view (making more profit). Anything that cuts the use of cars enough to cure the smog problem will cause major losses to a multitude of businesses. Politicians realize that such a readjustment may make the voters unpredictable. The debate goes on and the smog thickens.

This tragic reality is central to the discussions of major environmental crises across the country. The "death" of Lake Erie, strip mining for coal, drainage of the Everglades, and bay fill in San Francisco are all environmental problems that are immersed in a dialogue that is slow to produce a solution. These problems are well known, and it is widely agreed that something *must* be done to correct them. However, the politicians still try to be re-elected and businessmen still try to show a profit. The alternatives available to you and me are restricted by these political and economic "imperatives."

Ecological reality demands the recognition of universal absolutes that have a higher cultural value than re-election or profit. All people will lose if our planet continues to suffer degraded fertility. A lungful of poisonous air or a swallow of unhealthy water does not discern among presidents, paupers, policemen, or purse-snatchers. The public has watched the politician and the developers of short-

12

Basic frame of reference

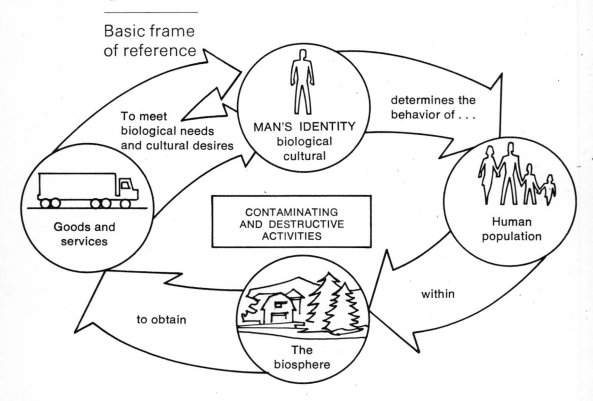

term profits and has grown increasingly pessimistic about changes that will save them from the avalanche of overpopulation and the related issues of war, food, and comfort. The public is beginning to understand that many practices of *all* industrialized societies have combined to spawn a situation that threatens our existence. Human survival can no longer be taken for granted. The human experience is in the process of being permanently changed. These changes will not be orderly, nor will they necessarily be constructive, from an ecological perspective, unless they are made carefully and consciously.

This chapter presents a frame of reference that can be used to give us an understanding of how we came to be immersed in this crisis; how our daily activities make it worse, and what actions we can take to assure our survival. This frame of reference begins with an individual's biological needs (food, warmth, and affection) and his cultural desires (material goods, prestige, leisure, etc.) It follows these needs and wants through the biosphere back to him when he is filled with food or his cultural desires are satisfied. How we go about securing food and other goods from the environment—and what number of people we secure them for—are the prime considerations as we map our future actions.

In the previous chapter we isolated the basic impacts of our doing these things in very uninformed and expedient ways. The result is destruction from 3.6 billion people feeding themselves and living in accordance with their native cultural systems. From analyzing how these wants and needs are generated and met, a basic frame of reference is outlined. Four main areas of activity form an information-flow pattern: human populations, man's identity, the biosphere, and goods and services. These activity and decision-making areas are linked together and shown in the illustration.

HUMAN POPULATIONS

Are we overpopulated? The answer depends on how we define overpopulation. Usually the people using this term do not define how they are using it, and so the considered response to this term is more often a very emotional one, rather than a considered answer. The existence of a condition known as overpopulation cannot be tied to number or growth rate. Such a number or rate would be arbitrary and very controversial. The ecological perspective does furnish us with a point of view from where we can define this term in a new way: Overpopulation exists when we are reducing the life-supporting capability of our surroundings.

Although we may still disagree as to what reduces our planet's fertility or when this occurs, it is more of an absolute than saying that overpopulation exists when it is too crowded. The definition also separates destruction of the life support system (overpopulation) from starvation of individuals, famine, and urban crowding. Starvation in many areas has more to do with the distribution system than with there being too many people. If it is not possible to feed those people in that area, given the ultimate in distribution and the area's productive limits, then that area is indeed overpopulated.

Overpopulation is then seen as a (hopefully) temporary condition that we can alleviate by understanding the limitations of our biosphere and bringing our behavior into harmony with it.

Present trends indicate the world's total number of people—three and one-half billion—will double by the year 2000. That is the equivalent of adding 318,000 people every day for the next thirty years! It is true that people are spread very irregularly over the earth's surface. More than two-thirds of the people live in Asia, and even in that area human populations are crowded into the coastal areas and great river basins. These areas usually have more rainfall for agriculture, and the ocean offers easy transport as well as a fishery to supplement food grains. In central and western Europe, as in the United States, population centers exist at historic trading sites, seaports, river junctions, and along railroads. The populations of Africa and Latin America are still basically rural, though the few cities are growing very rapidly.

These populations are increasing at different rates, and are made up of different proportions of young and old people. The differences that can be observed between the various populations, in terms of growth and age proportions, are largely due to the differences of impact from public health measures and other western innovations.

Developments in modern medicine assure that most people will live, raise families, and eat for a longer period of time. On first thought, it may seem that as a population reduces its death rate, it will have an older average age. In fact, modern medicine first affects the infant mortality rate, which results in more children, more adolescents, more marriages, more children, and a lower and lower average age for the population.

This demographic fact is true of every nation, including the technologically advanced nations, and means that the global population is expanding at a rate that is almost beyond comprehension. Even if each family has only two children, our numbers will double as the average age becomes the mean age. Just consider that it took man millions of years to reach the one billion population mark in 1830. We now have nearly four billion people on earth, and by the year 2000 will be up to the seven billion level.

MAN'S IDENTITY

What determines man's social and physical needs? What determines his aspirations or sense of priorities in relation to his community, his country, and the world? All men give high priority to survival— satisfying basic biological needs. In fact, most of us are at that level of existence, just barely gathering enough food, shelter, and clothing to keep alive for an average of 45 years. Those few, the wealthy minority, who have little day-to-day concern with survival needs, have a variety of opinions about things such as happiness and comfort and about what is necessary for emotional well-being.

46

"Man's identity" within this model is concerned with how his behavior affects planetary fertility. How does the fact of religion and the sacred cow affect 500,000,000 people on the Indian subcontinent? How does the fact of culture and the sacred car affect 200,000,000 people in the United States? Does their behavior in achieving their immediate goals, biological or cultural, increase planetary fertility, or does it decrease the chances of maintaining some balance between energy demands and energy sources?

While the cow and the car are both very important in their respective cultures, the host cultures differ in a very profound way. Traditional India does not have our notion of progress. The car in the American culture is a product of progress and is used to promote more "progress." The cow, on the other hand, has been used to maintain the agriculturally based village life of most of India. Many westerners feel that those cows are responsible for a large portion of India's problems. But without the cows, India could not plow her fields, would not have any fertilizer, would not have cooking fuel, and would not have an essential building material. (Cow manure is used by rural Indians as fuel for cooking and heating and as a plaster-like building material.) To do away with the cows would mean that fertilizer factories, roads, tractors, and trucks would have to be put into service, not to mention the money that would be needed by the average Indian to buy items that are now free.

In the United States we are almost as dependent on the car as India is on the cow. We would not get to work, school, or the market as conveniently without the car. While the cows may be competing with Indians for water and food, the car is competing with Americans for air and space. These considerations of cows and cars serve to indicate the extent to which man's identity is a cultural phenomenon. As we follow the path of the individual's need or desire through the frame of reference, we need to know as much about his cultural aspirations as we do about his biological requirements.

THE BIOSPHERE

All life is dependent on processes that occur within the biosphere. The ability of life to exist and reproduce depends upon the smooth functioning of all the ecosystems in the biosphere. When these diverse processes are interrupted or destroyed, some aspect of the planet's fertility has been diminished. *Planetary fertility* is a measure of how healthy all the processes within the biosphere are and to what degree they are endangered.

Let's examine a situation analogous to our present one. Imagine yourself and twenty-nine other people on a spaceship moving toward a habitable planet in another galaxy. The journey will take hundreds of years, and you must depend on the resources available on board the spaceship for your life support system. All your food, water, air, recreation, culture, and the like must be stored. Nothing can be wasted—not even human "waste products." We may have a clue about what this means by recalling what one of the Apollo 11 astronauts is alleged to have said: "Tonight's urine is tomorrow's Tang." Why not? What alternative is available? Certainly a whole generation's supply of water, food, and air cannot be loaded on board a space vehicle. Therefore everything must be recycled on our mythical venture if a healthy environment is to be maintained. What happens if all the couples on board decide to raise a family in preparation for colonizing planet X? To expand the spaceship's population beyond the capability of its life support system would mean suicide for all its occupants.

We have only touched on the problems of "spaceship travel," but now back to earth. Same problems: finite resources, limited energy sources, and a population that is doubling every fifty years or so. Nearly four billion humans are now making demands on the finite resources we have on board for our long voyage through space as we orbit the sun. While we understand that our life support is limited, we do not know how much we can increase our numbers or our consumption before there remains only self-destruction. We do know that the amount and quality of topsoil has been diminished, but we do not yet know how much of this is due to an excess of consumers and how much of it is due to ignorant and naive agricultural practices. We do know that we will run out of tungsten, copper, and nickel in the near future, but we don't know whether substitutes can be discovered or whether used metals can be cheaply recycled.

In summary, then, we can say that the life support system of Spaceship Earth is being diminished in many respects, and that the causes are probably excessive demands and the wasteful production of food and industrial products.

GOODS AND SERVICES

The term "goods and services" includes things to satisfy both our biological-survival needs and our cultural wants. This factor represents everything we obtain from our environment—dog collars, fishing hooks, candy bars, apples, and shoes, as well as Apollos and Skylarks. Enough people in the United States thought that all the expense and resources used for the Apollo project were more important than some other goods or services. Other cultures have decided that gold-leaf covered temples, stone pyramids, and mountaintop monasteries were an important use of scarce resources to satisfy their cultural beliefs and wants.

While biological needs must be satisfied as a condition of existence, cultural wants are a matter of value and preference. In our modern society it is not easy to separate these two factors. For instance, are automobiles necessary for survival needs, or are they merely an indication of cultural wants or psychological needs? In another instance, the farmland that has produced our lunch is probably unknown to us, yet we "need" the food it produces. To fulfill our nutritional requirements, we are dependent on many tools, implements, tractors, trucks, warehouses, and processing plants to prepare the food and deliver it to the store. This entire system of production and distribution reflects not only the need for food, but also the many cultural aspirations summed up in the phrases "the American way of life" or "the free enterprise system."

The world's societies structure their production-distribution systems in different ways as determined by their cultural backgrounds. Some may rely heavily on the traditional status of birth or rank that has been developed over thousands of years to determine how and by whom scarce goods and services are used. Other cultures may emphasize arbitrary economic decisions made by a few people in organizing their production and distribution systems.

It is important to examine the benefits and impacts of various past, present, and planned activities in light of both cultural and biological considerations.

ANALYZING SPECIFIC "HOUSEHOLD" IMPACTS

From an ecological viewpoint, short-term values or benefits may in fact be responsible for long-term "household" destruction or reduction in planetary fertility. Our responsibility as individuals and societies is to analyze various situations, using workable frames of reference or models, and to judge whether or not we are maintaining stable planetary resource balance. Figure 13 is a representation of how these four factors can change over time. This graph represents relative magnitudes rather than the physical size of anything.

13

Man's identity

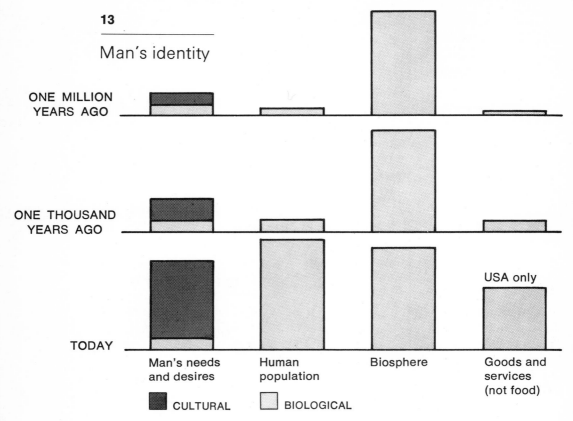

ONE MILLION
YEARS AGO

ONE THOUSAND
YEARS AGO

USA only

TODAY

| Man's needs and desires | Human population | Biosphere | Goods and services (not food) |

■ CULTURAL   □ BIOLOGICAL

The bars on this graph compare the situation in each category at three points in time. Note the items that have changed and those that remain constant.

Man's nature has changed more culturally than biologically. We are almost the same as we were thousands of years ago in our physiology, nutritional needs, brain functions, and so on. But we are very different in what we believe is important and necessary for us to do as people. We have values and aspirations related to the continuing development of technology and our standard of living. The graph shows man's identity increasing over time, but it is only his cultural identity that has increased in magnitude. For instance, in the past, man was forced to depend upon local food sources. Now we know of many other foods from around the world, and we create a demand for them. Refrigeration ships, warehouses, and trucks are all required to satisfy this cultural taste for a particular food that satisfies a biological need. Our cultural identity has also increased in the magnitude of desires for more and bigger objects fashioned from our surroundings. The baskets, bows, spears, rockpoints, te-pees, and canoes have evolved into supermarkets, nuclear weapons, carbon steel, skyscrapers, country homes, automobiles, jet planes, and ocean liners.

The rapid development of man's identity to this magnitude is true for western (or "westernized") countries. For many reasons, those cultures that are referred to as the "developing" countries have not experienced this cultural growth. These reasons would include such things as tired land, population pressures, lack of capital and natural resources, and the cultural desirability of "prog-ress." This differential development of man's cultural identity has to be taken into account when analyzing the world's situation and contemplating new programs.

Man's identity can be thought of as the individual *input* into human populations. This identity is what determines the various activities of the world's populations, including how many people there will be in a society. As man's cultural identity varies widely between geographic areas, so do the characteristics of the world's populations. Some are growing very fast, a few very slowly; some are composed of many old people, but most are made up of high percentages of young people.

The activities of populations in various stages of growth and development form the input or requests that we apply to the earth's surface and to the life support system. This system is composed of all the elements and processes that were mentioned in Chapter 1. Perhaps the recent Apollo missions have given us a new feeling for how finite and fragile this life support system is. If you look closely at the photographs of the planet's surface, you can see life's common household. The space between the clouds and the earth's surface is where all life activity takes place. That thin spherical film is shared by all life and furnishes us with the basic resources for all our needs and desires.

As the population on planet earth doubles, so do our biological requirements. But to push the limits of the environment's capacity even further, the wealthy nations of the world have been increasing their demands for goods and services much faster than their geo-metric population increases. Thus we can observe that societies representing the majority of the world's population have less to eat per person in 1970 than in 1950, while the wealthy minority have more and more goods and services per person every year.

The price of both the trials of poverty and the poisons of affluence, in terms of reduced fertility, may break all of us. In India, as has been previously explained, the cow is sacred and may not be eaten, but the cow's dung serves as valuable fertilizer and, when dried, as fuel for both cooking and heating. As India's population increases, there is greater demand for cow dung as a heat source, and less is available for fertilizer. The less fertilizer, the lower crop production per acre; the less food production in the face of population increase, the closer India comes to a cataclysmic famine.

California's population doubles every twenty years. Californians are richer on the average than they have ever been, and their demands for goods and services are almost insatiable: two and three cars per family, new houses in the suburbs, and miles of new freeway clogged by automobiles with their single occupants impatiently waiting to come or go. By conservative estimates, 50% of California's prime cropland will go to housing and industry in the next thirty years. Pessimists believe it will be 80%. In other words, the leading agricultural state in the union may give up 80% of its food production.

Are Californians wiser than Indians? Population up, food-producing area down—a rather disturbing situation, no matter where it occurs. Something else to consider, in both California and India, is that we are clearing the land of oxygen *producers* (plants and trees) to make room for oxygen *consumers*.

Or consider this situation. Before technological development, man's total impact in an ecosystem was confined to the local area. It involved clearing a few trees to make room for houses and gardens, cutting firewood, and gathering clay for pots. As man's projects became bigger and bigger, entire regions were affected adversely. The best example of this exists in the Mediterranean region. Deforestation, irrigation, intensive agriculture, then siltation of the ditches and salination of fields, and finally massive erosion, resulting in large and widespread climatic changes. Whatever happened to the Garden of Eden, the "fertile crescent," the Cedars of Lebanon, and the University of Timbuctu? It is thought that similar sequences of man-caused destruction have occurred throughout the Middle East, Africa, and the European Mediterranean, as well as in South and Central America.

Finally, the industrial revolution has brought about the realities of global impacts from the activities of a single culture. Hard pesticides, the chlorinated hydrocarbons such as DDT, radioactive fallout, lead, mercury and other substances and chemicals are having detrimental effects on all of the world's major ecosystems.

52

ANALYZING MAN'S ACTIONS IN
THE BIOSPHERE: THE CASE OF DDT

The states of Michigan and California have at least partially banned the chlorinated hydrocarbon, dichloro-diphenyl-trichloroethane (DDT). The federal government expresses concern at the widespread use of DDT, agricultural industrialists express concern, and we, the quiet vegetable eaters, express concern. Even though the use of DDT is restricted and may be banned, many tons are still in the environment. Some is still "loose," and some is in each of us and other living things. The effects of this and other chemicals will continue to appear long after we stop using them. By using a conceptual tool, such as the ecology reference model, we can examine the benefits and dangers of using DDT. This frame of reference will also allow us to follow a pathway back from both the benefits and dangers to the human decision or need that led to the existence of DDT.

Because, as shown in the illustration, we are looking at something that has already happened, and we know something of its

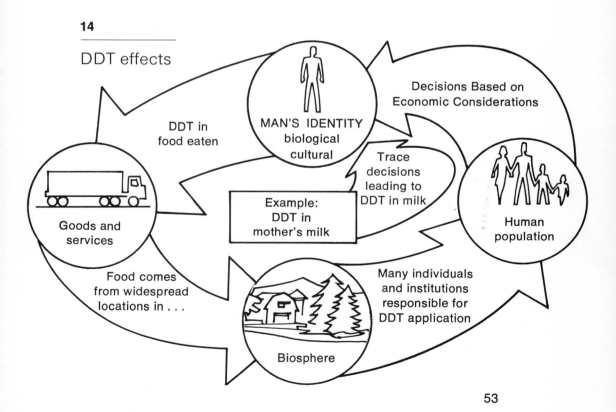

14

DDT effects

DDT in food eaten

MAN'S IDENTITY biological cultural

Decisions Based on Economic Considerations

Trace decisions leading to DDT in milk

Goods and services

Example: DDT in mother's milk

Human population

Food comes from widespread locations in . . .

Many individuals and institutions responsible for DDT application

Biosphere

impact, we can start by entering data into the box labeled "destruction." Consider the species that are now seriously threatened with extinction by chlorinated hydrocarbons, as well as any evidence of harmful effects on other life forms. Most of the investigative work has been done for us. We know that (1) traces of DDT are found everywhere—even in the penguins of Antarctica; (2) animals accumulate DDT in fat tissues, in such a way that it cannot be passed through normal waste-removing functions; (3) animals at the end of complex food chains accumulate the DDT ingested by the organisms that precede them in the food chain; (4) DDT causes a breakdown in the internal chemistry of birds so that they give birth to young with no shells, or with shells so fragile that they break under the weight of a nesting parent; (5) analysis of the milk of nursing mothers both in England and the United States shows a DDT content higher than that allowed in cow's milk by the U.S. Department of Public Health; (6) it has been shown in laboratory experiments that DDT hinders photosynthesis in phytoplankton.

After entering all of the above impacts in the central block (destruction), we can trace each impact backward until it can be understood as an expression of one or many individual wants or needs. For instance, let's trace back the DDT in mother's milk. Start in the block that represents its present location. In this case, this would be biological woman. Where did the DDT come from? The food she has been eating. Draw an arrow back to goods and services. Where does the food come from? From those portions of the biosphere where her food was grown: a wheat field in Montana, a potato field in Idaho, rice paddies in California, orchards in many states, and a dairy near her home town. From all these locations in the environment, we trace the DDT back through the population block, all the people in the agencies and firms that had anything to do with the necessity for, invention of, and manufacture of it. As none of those people needed or wanted DDT itself to satisfy biological requirements, we can say that the use of DDT was a decision made by cultural man to satisfy biological man in culturally prescribed ways. "Culturally prescribed ways" refers to such things as mono-agriculture and consumer preference for aesthetically pleasing produce.

The same general procedure can be followed for all of the other known impacts from the use of DDT, which is an example of household contamination, the deliberate application of chemicals.

At this point it appears that the combined impact of the biological requirements of our large populations and their cultural aspirations cause a measurable decrease in the planet's fertility. We could also determine the actual path of DDT from the point of manufacture to mother's milk or to penguins. The path would include warehouses and railroads as well as rain and irrigation water rinsing the DDT off the farmland into the ocean, and wind currents delivering it to water surfaces, where it is taken up into the marine food chain, and therein concentrated in several steps until it is eaten by man, penguin or peregrine falcon. The peregrine falcon population collapsed first because the falcon preys on marine birds that eat fish; pelicans were affected next, perhaps because they eat relatively large fish that have eaten other fish. That leaves man, who eats only a few fish, but eats them over a longer span of time than falcons or penguins.

The public knowledge of the harmful effects of DDT, combined with our knowledge of farmers' dependence on it, is an example of psychological contamination of our household.

Similar psychological binds exist for each of the household impacts. And each impact can be examined from several points of view. For example, as insects become immune to DDT, increased applications of pesticides are needed to maintain the food production necessary to meet the demands for food to satisfy man's biological requirements. As more DDT is used to control the increasingly immune bugs, the pesticide accumulates in higher quantities in the systems of other organisms, leading to consequences that may be recorded in both the biological part of *human nature* and in total *populations* of various creatures within the biosphere.

To gauge the benefits of DDT is very difficult, as we do not know what would be the total result of not using DDT. Biologists seem to be divided on the necessity of using pesticides and insecticides.* A complicating factor is the aspect of the size of the fields and the layout of the crops, for large areas growing only one kind of plant are extremely unnatural and unstable. It is not clear that the use of DDT results in more or better food. Perhaps the only

---

*We must keep in mind that DDT is only one of many high-impact synthetic chemical pesticides. There are closely related *chlorinated hydrocarbons,* compounds such as aldrin, dieldrin, heptachlor, and toxaphene, which are much more toxic than DDT. Although they last a shorter time and are sometimes slightly more specific in which insects they kill, they are nevertheless long-lasting and widely destructive. In addition, there are other chemicals, both better and worse. The *organophosphates,* such as malathion, TEPP, and SEVIN, are highly toxic and very dangerous to humans; some kill all insects and some kill specific insects. They are generally much less persistent than the chlorinated hydrocarbons.

benefit possible is the economic one of using an inexpensive preventive. But then, it must be realized that DDT is not pest-specific and sometimes does more harm to a pest's natural enemy that to the "pest." Another problem in comparing impact with benefit is the time factor. The peregrine falcon's distress was not discovered until 1968, but DDT has been in use in the United States since the late 1940's. Economic gains are figured on a yearly basis, and so conceivably twenty years of economic benefit could be shown as against only two years of adverse effects. But the falcon may be gone forever, while the farmer will go on farming. The accounting system would be very difficult: how much would it cost to clean DDT from the household's food chains? How much is lost by the extinction of a few wild birds?

CHAPTER FIVE

Cultural Response to Ecology

The ecology reference model is a tool for locating and analyzing man's impact on the biosphere. Using this framework, we can clarify our situation. Man, individually and collectively, is at a threshold in his evolution. Three distinct periods can be noted. Archaeological records and anthropological evidence indicate a period of *emergence,* then one of *world settlement* (establishment of aboriginal populations), and finally, the present period of *population explosion.* This present period started with the discovery of agriculture and then the rapid development of technology, joined by a short period of very rapid emigration from Europe to the New World.

This last age has been marked by almost complete cultural ignorance of the life support system, particularly among modern western nations. For reasons we are just beginning to comprehend, man developed without an understanding of his dependence upon it. We have become comfortable with our own present activities, and it is very difficult to grasp the reality that what we are doing at present may be very harmful. The evidence seems to suggest that if present activities are continued, we will drastically diminish household fertility and precipitate wholesale death for people, fish, insects, plants, and animals. The next age is yet to be named. It could be a short one wherein human populations decimate themselves and enter into a dark age. Or it could be an age of global reclamation projects, population stabilization, and disarmament. Such an age of ecological reform will not come unless many people demand it.

Our present situation could be summed up as being one of ecological illiteracy. We cannot say that it is certain we will extinguish all life by a certain date; we do not have adequate information. All we can be sure of is our continuing reduction of planetary fertility. We do not know for sure how much longer we can continue present practices and still expect the earth to provide for our needs and desires. Nor do we know if damage beyond a certain point will start a spontaneous process of degradation and destruction beyond our capabilities to correct.

Some authors present horrible pictures of future years. Others, notably Herman Kahn, present a picture of technological innovations that will solve most of man's problems. Many individuals who know about the ecological crisis and feel that it is a survival issue are upset that government and other institutions are moving so slowly. It should be realized that social institutions cannot move on a cultural issue until there is public consensus for such movement. If *everyone* waits for such a consensus, we will wait a long time; someone or some groups must take the lead. Cultural change cannot be written into legislation or funded with special programs or facilitated by government. Culture is lived. If the culture indeed must be changed, many people have to live differently, and someone has to start.

Every action and habit should be evaluated in terms of its possible cumulative impact on the "household." Our impact on the forests comes partly from our demands for paper that we do not have the time to bundle up and take to a collection bin for recycling. If there is no such bin, then build one! As the forests are wasted one sheet at a time, they will be saved one sheet at a time. Smog also is largely the result of individual preferences. For instance, we live at considerable distances from our friends, jobs, and supply centers, and so we need transportation. The form of transportation we prefer is the private automobile, which has a deadly impact on our planet.

While some preferences cannot be overcome by individual action, many can. Witness the high school students who walked or rode their bicycles to school and the nursing mothers who became concerned about the DDT their infants were ingesting. As individuals change their life style, the culture will be transformed and will become receptive to new and innovative programs from government.

This kind of social change requires an anticipation, by all people, of the implications of ecology. Only through empathy with our planet will we be able to move a little bit each day toward a life style that protects our planet's fertility. If we cannot act and think for ourselves in response to new understanding, we are indeed on the way to extinction.

Population demand vs. life support system

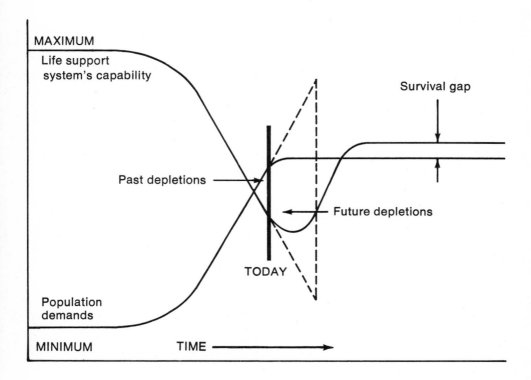

This graph is a conceptual tool. The crossover of the two basic curves represents the point in time when the rate at which we were extracting materials and energy from the life support system and in other ways reducing its capabilities became greater than the rate at which the system could recycle and rejuvenate, and we began to use up the system itself. This is as if the demands of a family had increased to a point where they could no longer live off the interest on money they had in the bank and began to withdraw this capital. At some point they will withdraw the last of the capital and no interest will be generated. The dashed lines on the graph indicate such a possibility for the earth. To prevent such a possibility from happening, we must reduce or at least stabilize population demand while restoring the life support system to a level sufficiently high to provide a survival gap, a buffer zone between population demand and the ability of the earth to support life without destruction of the system for doing so. The longer we hesitate the more difficult the job of restoration will be. At some point it may become impossible.

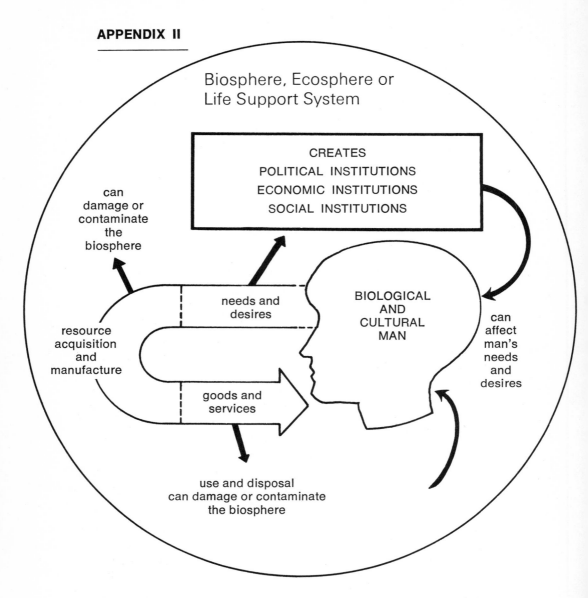

This diagram is an expansion of the frames of reference on page 44. It can be used to help trace the cause-and-effect relationships of almost all of the things discussed in the course of this book. For example, any damage or contamination of the biosphere can be traced back to resource acquisition, manufacturing, or the use and disposal of goods and services needed by the biological part of man's identity or desired by the cultural part of his identity. In the process, institutions are created which can cause changes in these needs and desires by developing a course in ecology for instance or advertising an automobile.

INDEX

A

Africa, 35, 46, 52
Agricultural methods, 42
  damage caused by, 42, 52, 55
  DDT, 53–56
  deserts, 32
  dust bowl, 33
  forest clearing, 34–35
  impact on biosphere, 27, 42, 52
  increase in erosion, 42, 52
  India, 47
  salination, 42, 52
Air, volume of, 7
Algae, 25, 29, 30
Alpine lake, 30
Alpine tundra: *See* Tundra
Ammonia (nitrogen cycle), 20
Animals, 5, 13–14, 25, 26, 28, 29
  biogeochemical cycles, 19–20
  carnivores, 13, 14
  desert, 31–32
  food chains, 13
  food pyramids, 14, 15
  grazing, 16, 33
  herbivores, 13, 14
  migratory, 33
  predators, 13
  "sacred cow," 47
  tidal areas, 29
  tundra, 33;
  See also Birds; Fish.
Anza-Borrego Desert (Calif.), 32
Apollo 11, 48
Arable land: *See* Farmland
Arctic tundra: *See* Tundra
Aristotle, 21
Asia, 46; *See also* India
Atmosphere, 19, 20, 21, 37
Atomic energy, 12, 13
  disadvantages, 12;
  See also Radioactivity
Automobiles, 36, 41, 58
  compared with sacred cow, 47

effects on U.S. culture, 47, 49
internal combustion engine, 43

B

Biogeochemical cycles, 18–19, 36
Biological needs of man, 44, 46–47, 48–49
  basic frame of reference, 44
  changes over time, 50
  relation to DDT, 54
Biological organization, levels of, 17
Biologist, range of study of, 17
Biosphere, 8, 47
  basic ecological frame of reference, 44–45, 57
  components, 7, 8
  DDT, 53–56
  effects of man's actions, 53–56
  level of organization, 17
  major ecosystems, 25–35
  population demand, 59
Birds, 5, 18, 22, 25
  effect of DDT, 54, 55, 56
  Galapagos finches, 21–23
  marine, 15, 23–24
  territoriality, 24
  tundra, 33
Bread, nutritional value of, 39
Brown, Dr. Harrison, 37

C

California
  agricultural practices, 32
  ban on DDT, 53
  goods and services, 52
  population trends, 52
Carbon dioxide (CO_2), 10, 11
  carbon-oxygen cycles, 19
  "greenhouse effect," 38–39
  plant material, 13

released by combustion, 11, 37–39
  stored in oceans, 28
Carbon-oxygen cycles, 19
Carnivores, 13–14
Chemical contamination, 41
Cities
  noise pollution, 41
  smog, 43
  urban crowding, 45
Climatic changes, 52
  See also Temperature, global
Climax (evolution), 25
  forest, 26, 27
Clouds, 9–10
Coal mining, 40, 42, 43
Coniferous forest:
  See Forests
Cultural desires, of man, 44, 46–47, 48–49, 58
  basic frame of reference, 44, 58
  changes over time, 50
  effects on production-distribution system, 49
  relationship to DDT, 54
  response to ecology, 57–59
Cultural growth, 50–51
Cultural identity, 50–51;
  See also Man's identity
Cuyahoga River (Ohio), 30

D

Darwin, Charles, 21
  dynamics of evolution, 22
DDT, 52, 53–56
  case history of man's actions, 53–56
  effects of, 53, 54
  food, in, 28
  mothers' milk, in, 5, 53, 54, 58
  ocean food chains, in, 28
  sources of, 54
Death rate, 46
Deciduous forest:
  See Forests

61